A CHILD'S BOOK OF MANNERS

Preschool Activity and Coloring Fun

based on the book by Ruth Shannon Odor
developed by Greg Holder and Diane Stortz
illustrated by Jodie McCallum

The Standard Publishing Company, Cincinnati, Ohio
A division of Standex International Corporation
© 1995 by The Standard Publishing Company
All rights reserved.
Printed in the United States of America
ISBN 0-7847-0282-9

Good manners begin at home.

Close doors quietly.
"Door" starts with "D."
Circle all the objects in this picture that begin with "D."

Put away your toys.

Draw a line between each toy and the place it belongs.

Help make mealtimes happy.

At the table, don't talk with your mouth full.
Circle the five things that are wrong with this picture.

Say "Please" if you want something.
Say "Thank you" when you are given something.
Say "No, thank you" when you do not want something.

*Draw a line
from each picture
to the polite words
that should be said.*

Thank you.

No, thank you.

Please.

If you want to leave the table,
ask, "May I be excused?"
If a grown-up says yes,
answer, "Thank you."

Circle these things in the picture.
- fork
- spoon
- bowl
- plate
- cup
- napkin

Don't be like

Shoveler Shawn,

Picky Pete,

Susie the Slurper,

or Messy Bessy.

Circle the kids in each row who are eating neatly.

Friends don't just happen.
If you want a friend, you have to be one.

Take turns when you play.
Connect the dots to see what these friends are doing.

Share your snacks.
Finish the picture by drawing your favorite snack.

When you play a game, play fair.
Circle seven things you use for playing games.

Jesus said we should treat others the way we want to be treated.

Don't be like

Me-First Megan . . .

Look-at-Me Louie . . .

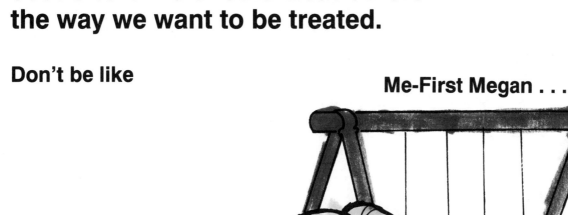

That's Mine Tracy.

Color the swing set red.
Color the skateboard green.
Color the teddy bear blue.

Always tell the truth — even when it is not easy.
Help the girl find her mother
so she can tell the truth.

Don't disturb others who are trying to listen.

Find four children who are listening and not disturbing others.

**If we try to be like Jesus in all we say and do,
then having good manners will be as easy as . . .**

*Trace the letters and numbers
to complete the sentence.*